LifeBook

Household Information System

LifeBook

Published by Easy Life Publications LLC
PO Box 9172
Asheville, NC   28815-0172

Library of Congress Cataloging-in-Publication Data is available.

ISBN-13: 978-0-9960537-0-9

Manufactured in USA

For information about LifeBook
and Easy Life Publications, please visit
ezlifebook.com

Welcome to LifeBook

We lead busy lives. We're frequently on the run juggling various errands and tasks but we often find that we don't have the necessary information at hand to complete them. We sometimes drop the ball. We face the daunting challenge of maintaining ever greater amounts of information to keep our households running smoothly. It's frustrating and time-consuming when we find it necessary to track down information from various sources. And it's even more frustrating when we can't locate the information at all. It's time to turn to LifeBook.

LifeBook is a household information management system designed to help you organize names, contact information, passwords, model numbers, medications, bank accounts, insurance policies, and many other types of key information. It's an easy-to-use method of managing the record-keeping that goes along with the contemporary, information-laden home. It allows you to customize and update information in a simple but effective way, so that it is easily retrievable by anyone who needs it.

LifeBook will prove useful when multiple family members share the organization and completion of household tasks but not always the information needed to complete those tasks. LifeBook can be a great resource if you're absent for extended periods and your home is left in the charge of others who are less familiar with its operation. Should an emergency arise in which information is vital to your home or personal security, LifeBook can be invaluable.

LifeBook is YOUR book. You can add information and make changes at your convenience. Make it available to household members and those who share in the complex organization of your life. A free digital LifeBook is available in Excel format for download at **ezlifebook.com**. You can use it to electronically update and access LifeBook on your computer or mobile device.

LifeBook will contain personal information so keep it in a safe place.

How to Use LifeBook

LifeBook is designed to work in tandem with your other existing methods of home organization. It's a breeze to use. Each data entry category is a module. All modules contain data entry tabs organized into convenient headings. Enter as much or as little information as you need.

Enter your household information anytime at your convenience. Once you've entered your information into the LifeBook modules, it will be easy to keep it current and relevant. Each module contains a "My Notes" data entry tab, which allows you to customize its content by adding or updating information.

LifeBook is YOUR book. Manage it in any manner that suits your needs.

Many of you may prefer to manage your LifeBook in an electronic format. For this purpose, we have produced LifeBook as an MS Excel-based system for use on your computer. It's free. You can access the Electronic LifeBook as a free download by going to **ezlifebook.com**. Follow the simple directions on the web page.

TIP: Works best with a pencil.

LifeBook

Module Navigator

Appliances Module

 Refrigerators

 Oven / Stove

 Dishwasher

 Microwave Oven

 Freezer

 Furnace / Heat Pump

 Water Heater

 Gas Fireplace

Appliances

Performing significant repairs to a household appliance is best left to a trained professional. However, you can sometimes minimize maintenance costs by performing routine maintenance and cleaning tasks yourself.

Computerization has caught up with most of our household appliances so the days of plug-in-and-go are just about over. For example, when you acquire a new appliance, to get started you may be faced with a digital clock and other features that must be programmed. It tends to get more complicated from that point onward.

Keeping all of your appliances functioning as designed requires quick and easy access to key information. This module is designed to help you achieve that.

Here are some examples of the types of information you may want to record in this module:

Identification and Documentation

- Appliance makes, model numbers and serial numbers
- Power sources (electricity, natural gas, propane, fuel oil, solar)

Assemble owner manuals, warranty documentation and your purchase receipts in one strategic location and record that location in LifeBook.

Shut-Off Instructions
Natural Gas, Propane and Electricity

If the energy source for a particular appliance is natural gas or propane, there will be a shut-off valve that must be closed in an emergency. Record shut-off valve locations and outline the procedures for operating the valves.

TIP: An electrical appliance may have its own circuit. In the event of an appliance malfunction, you may need to turn off power to that circuit at the circuit breaker box. That's why your circuit breaker box should be clearly labeled with the name of each appliance or room in the house.

Service and Repair

For each major appliance, record the service specialist contact information so you can quickly schedule service when needed. If the manufacturer specifies that only authorized service providers can provide warranty service, make a note of that and record contact information for those providers.

Refrigerators

Make, Model, and Serial Number

Service and Repair

Date of Purchase Warranty

Document Locations

My Notes

LifeBook

Oven / Stove

Make, Model, and Serial Number

Service and Repair

Date of Purchase Warranty

Document Locations

My Notes

Dishwasher

Make, Model, and Serial Number

Service and Repair

Date of Purchase Warranty

Document Locations

My Notes

LifeBook

Microwave Oven

Make, Model, and Serial Number

Service and Repair

Date of Purchase Warranty

Document Locations

My Notes

Clothes Washer/Dryer

Make, Model, and Serial Number

Service and Repair

Date of Purchase Warranty

Document Locations

My Notes

Freezer

Make, Model, and Serial Number

Service and Repair

Date of Purchase Warranty

Document Locations

My Notes

Furnace/Heat Pump

Make, Model, and Serial Number

Service and Repair

Date of Purchase Warranty

Document Locations

My Notes

LifeBook

Water Heater

Make, Model, and Serial Number

Service and Repair

Date of Purchase Warranty

Document Locations

My Notes

Gas Fireplace

Make, Model, and Serial Number

Service and Repair

Date of Purchase Warranty

Document Locations

My Notes

Notes

Notes

LifeBook

Home Mechanics Module

 Utility Systems

 Interior Systems

 Exterior Systems

 Well / Sump Pump

 Garage Door Opener

 Garden Lights & Ponds

Home Mechanics

Most of us maintain some aspects of our household mechanical systems: fixing faucets, changing light bulbs, replacing furnace filters, and so forth. Our household mechanics are becoming more sophisticated with advancing technology and in some cases are computer-controlled and beyond our technical expertise (see Professional Services module). The regular maintenance of our household mechanics is necessary for daily living and helps to preserve the value of our home.

This module asks you to think about the following home mechanical functions:

- Utility, water, and sewage systems
- Heating and cooling systems

Interruptions in the function of these systems may cause inconvenience, costly repairs, and even health concerns for you and your family.

Take inventory of your home's mechanical systems. Determine the types of systems you have, making note of manufacturer, model numbers, locations and operation of controls. Make a record of them here. Doing so now will help you avoid searching for them in the dark or when time is critical!

Utility Systems

Water Service Provider

Waterline Location Notes

Sewage Service Provider

Septic Tank Location Notes

Gas / Electricity Service Providers

Gas / Electricity Location Notes

Other

My Notes

Interior Systems

Climate Control

Security

Energy and Power

Water Treatment / Purifier

My Notes

LifeBook

Exterior Systems

Lawn and Garden Irrigation

Lighting and Security

My Notes

Well/Sump Pump

Make, Model, and Serial Number

Service and Repair

Date of Purchase Warranty

Document Locations

My Notes

LifeBook

Garage Door Opener

Make, Model, and Serial Number

Service and Repair

Date of Purchase Warranty

Document Locations

My Notes

Garden Lights / Pond

Make, Model, and Serial Number

Service and Repair

Date of Purchase Warranty

Document Locations

My Notes

LifeBook

Notes

Notes

LifeBook

Digital Communications Module

Device One

Device Two

Device Three

Digital Communications

With each passing day, we rely more heavily on our computers, internet modems, wi-fi routers, mobile devices, printers and other tools to help us manage our professional and personal lives.

To maintain your digital communications world, you need at least a basic understanding of the technologies involved. You also need to be able to quickly access certain types of information such as device specifications, log-in names and passwords, network addresses, contact numbers for service technicians and service providers, and more.

This module is designed to help you organize all of your digital communications information in one place so it's there when you need it. Here are some examples of the types of information you may want to record in this module:

Identification and Documentation

- Device make, model and serial number, operating system and specifications
- Your log-in and password for each of your devices
- Your wi-fi network address
- Contact information and your account number for your Internet service provider

Assemble user manuals, warranty documentation and purchase receipts in one strategic location and record that location in LifeBook. For online user manuals, note their locations on your computer.

TIP: Power outages frequently interrupt Internet service and may require rebooting your modem. Keep handy the instructions for doing this as well as the pertinent device information in case you need to follow-up with a phone call to your service provider.

Software and Virus Protection

- File names and file locations on your device
- Intervals and procedures for updating your virus protection

Computer Back-Up Systems

- File names and file locations on your device
- Intervals and procedures for performing the back-up procedure

Build Your Reference Library

- Reset procedures for your internet modem and wi-fi router
- Additional reference sources (websites, etc.) you use for troubleshooting your devices
- Your notes about performing certain procedures when using software or apps so you'll have that information on hand the next time you need to perform those procedures
- Reference sources you can access when you have a question about software features

Technical Support and Service/Repair

For each device, record the contact information for technical support or hardware service. If the manufacturer specifies that only authorized service providers can provide warranty service, make a note of it and record the contact information for those providers.

Device One

Log-In, User Name, and Password

Internet / Cellular Service Providers

Make, Model, and Serial Number

Operating System

System Properties (Processor, RAM, and System Type)

Virus Protection

Back-Up System (Hard-Drive, USB, Cloud)

LifeBook

Technical Support
and Service / Repair

Date of Purchase
Warranty

Document Locations

My Notes

Device Two

Log-In, User Name, and Password

Internet / Cellular Service Providers

Make, Model, and Serial Number

Operating System

System Properties (Processor, RAM, and System Type)

Virus Protection

Back-Up System (Hard-Drive, USB, Cloud)

LifeBook

**Technical Support
and Service / Repair**

**Date of Purchase
Warranty**

Document Locations

My Notes

Device Three

Log-In, User Name, and Password

Internet / Cellular Service Providers

Make, Model, and Serial Number

Operating System

System Properties (Processor, RAM, and System Type)

Virus Protection

Back-Up System (Hard-Drive, USB, Cloud)

LifeBook

**Technical Support
and Service / Repair**

**Date of Purchase
Warranty**

Document Locations

My Notes

Notes

LifeBook

Digital Entertainment Module

Device One

Device Two

Device Three

Digital Entertainment

We live in an age when we can enjoy high-tech digital entertainment components and systems that we couldn't have even imagined just a few short years ago. The typical household might include any of the following:

- Smart HD TVs and associated devices
- Home theater systems
- Projectors and screens
- Blue-ray and DVD players
- Digital tuners and converters
- Digital cable service modems
- Satellite dishes

Your need for information begins when you connect and program any of these components and systems. (As we know, this is not always the "piece of cake" promised by your friendly salesperson.) And once everything is up and running you periodically need key information in order to enjoy all of the available features and to troubleshoot problems. This module is designed to help you organize the information you might need so you can spend your time enjoying your digital entertainment world instead of hunting for the information that operates it.

Here are some examples of the types of information you may want to record in this module:

Identification and Documentation

- Component make, model number, serial number, and specifications
- Contact information and your account number for your internet service provider

Assemble user manuals, warranty documentation, and purchase receipts in one strategic location and record that location in LifeBook. For online user manuals, note their locations on your computer.

Build Your Reference Library

- Reset procedures for your cable modem
- Additional references sources (websites, etc.) you use for troubleshooting your components and systems
- Your notes about using certain features so you'll have that information on hand the next time you want to use those features

Technical Support and Service Providers

For each component and system, record the contact information for technical support or hardware service. If the manufacturer specifies that only authorized service providers can provide warranty service, make a note of it and record the contact information for those providers.

Device One

Device Type and Service Provider

Make, Model, and Serial Number

Technical Support and Service /Repair

Date of Purchase Warranty

Document Locations

My Notes

LifeBook

Device Two

Device Type and Service Provider

Make, Model, and Serial Number

Technical Support and Service /Repair

Date of Purchase Warranty

Document Locations

My Notes

Device Three

Device Type and Service Provider

Make, Model, and Serial Number

Technical Support and Service /Repair

Date of Purchase Warranty

Document Locations

My Notes

LifeBook

Notes

Notes

LifeBook

Finance
Module

 Financial
Advisors

 Beneficiaries

 Banking
Institutions

 Income

 Debt

 Investments

 Other
Financial

Finance

You plan and budget so that you can maintain a sound financial footing in the present while also planning for your financial future. Steering your financial ship in the right direction requires that you make periodic course corrections, ideally with the help of financial advisors, accountants, and other professionals. But it's up to you to maintain the information you and your financial team need to continuously evaluate your course and, if necessary, make adjustments for your household's long-term financial security.

You also need accurate, timely financial information on a day-to-day basis in order to effectively manage your financial life in a number of important areas, including the following:

- Budgeting for emergencies
- Making decisions that impact your income such as a career or job change
- Making decisions that impact your expenses such as a new home or a new vehicle
- Understanding your tax liabilities and gathering documentation required to complete your tax returns

TIP: This module is not a substitute for long-term financial planning or a household budget. It is designed to help you maintain your financial information in categories so you can quickly access specific information anytime you need it.

Privacy

Depending upon the complexity of our household financial system, this module may be quite large. This is PRIVATE information, so keep it safe!

Financial Advisors

Accountant

Financial Advisor / Stock Broker

Tax Attorney

Power of Attorney

My Notes

Beneficiaries

Financial Beneficiaries

Will (Location and Contact Information)

Trust Account

My Notes

Banking

Savings Account

Checking Account

Certificates of Deposit (CDs)

Credit Union Accounts

Safe Deposit Box

My Notes

Income

Primary Job

Secondary Job

Other Income

My Notes

Debt

Home Mortgage

Credit Cards

Lines of Credit

**Other Loans
(Education, Auto, Etc.)**

My Notes

Stocks and Bonds

Annuities

Real Estate

Retirement Accounts and Pensions

My Notes

Other Financial

Charities

Dues and Subscriptions

Letters of Instruction

My Notes

Notes

LifeBook

Government Agencies Module

Local Government

State Government

Federal Government

Government Agencies

We often have a need to contact government offices and are encouraged to voice our concerns to elected officials. It helps to understand the various levels of government agencies – local or city government, county, state, and federal – and to know their responsibilities.

Law enforcement, fire protection, and emergency responders are available in times of emergency through local 911 emergency contact systems. More commonly, though, we must rummage through various directories to find the proper office to contact. Road departments operate locally and also at the county level. Politicians work at all levels and include our mayor and city commissioners, county officials, state senators and congressional representatives, and United States senators and congressmen. Some offices we contact on a regular basis, for example the Secretary of State for vehicle issues, the Register of Deeds office for real estate matters, and the County Health Department, while others provide assistance in times of emergency or special need.

In this module, you will find data entry pages for commonly-queried offices at local, state, and federal levels. Enter names and contact information so you can easily contact them.

LifeBook

Local Government

Mayor's Office

Road Commission

Tax Office

Property and Deeds

School Board

Health Department

Parks and Recreation Department

County Clerk's Office

Other Local Agencies

My Notes

State Government

Secretary of State

Local State Congressman

State Senator

Other State Agencies

My Notes

LifeBook

Federal Government

Congressional District Number

U.S. Senator

U.S. Congressman

Post Office

Social Security Office

Other Federal Agencies

My Notes

Notes

LifeBook

Health and Well-Being Module

 Health Care Providers

 Prescriptions and Medications

 Personal History

Health and Well-Being

Our personal well-being depends upon access to the most current and accurate information about our health and medications. This is a cornerstone of the nation's health delivery systems and it also should be the foundation for your household health and wellness system. This module helps you organize information for health providers and caregivers, including health histories and medication records for you and your family. Having accurate records at hand will help you avoid hazardous mix-ups that have potentially life-threatening consequences. By keeping a clear focus on your own history, along with your doctor's recommendations, you can avoid being unduly influenced by medical marketing and stay in charge of your own health and well-being.

TIP: Think in terms of both preventive efforts to maintain your own personal good health and what a first responder might need to know about you and your family in the case of a medical emergency. Blood type, drug and food allergies, current medications, and past surgeries are all things that persons trying to help you will want to know.

It will be helpful to maintain separate data entry fields for each member of your household.

Health Care Providers

family member's name

Primary Physician	
Specialist	
Dentist	
Dermatologist	
Chiropractor	
Other Wellness Providers	
Emergency Care Clinic	
Hospital	
Health Care Advocate	
My Notes	

Health Care Providers

family member's name

Primary Physician

Specialist

Dentist

Dermatologist

Chiropractor

Other Wellness Providers

Emergency Care Clinic

Hospital

Health Care Advocate

My Notes

LifeBook

Health Care Providers

family member's name

Primary Physician	
Specialist	
Dentist	
Dermatologist	
Chiropractor	
Other Wellness Providers	
Emergency Care Clinic	
Hospital	
Health Care Advocate	
My Notes	

Health Care Providers

family member's name

Primary Physician

Specialist

Dentist

Dermatologist

Chiropractor

Other Wellness Providers

Emergency Care Clinic

Hospital

Health Care Advocate

My Notes

LifeBook

Prescriptions and Medications

family member's name

Prescribed Drugs

**Supplements
and Vitamins**

Other Medications

My Notes

family member's name

Prescribed Drugs

Supplements and Vitamins

Other Medications

My Notes

Prescriptions and Medications

family member's name

Prescribed Drugs

Supplements and Vitamins

Other Medications

My Notes

Prescriptions and Medications

family member's name

Prescribed Drugs

Supplements and Vitamins

Other Medications

My Notes

LifeBook

Personal History

family member's name

Blood Type

Drug Allergies

Food Allergies

Environmental Allergies

Surgeries (with Dates)

Chronic Conditions

My Notes

Personal History

family member's name

Blood Type

Drug Allergies

Food Allergies

Environmental Allergies

Surgeries (with Dates)

Chronic Conditions

My Notes

LifeBook

Personal History

family member's name

Blood Type

Drug Allergies

Food Allergies

Environmental Allergies

Surgeries (with Dates)

Chronic Conditions

My Notes

Personal History

family member's name

Blood Type

Drug Allergies

Food Allergies

Environmental Allergies

Surgeries (with Dates)

Chronic Conditions

My Notes

LifeBook

Notes

Notes

Insurance Module

 Home

 Health and Life

 Beneficiaries

 Business

 Vehicles

Insurance

Insurance is a necessity of modern life. If you live a simple life, your insurance needs may be minimal. Other households will have myriad insurance policies covering everything from pets to airplanes.

Most insurance companies offer discounted packages to "bundle" various insurances needs. This can make it simpler to negotiate premiums and to manage your insurance policies. With bundled coverage, you will have a single agent that handles the majority of your insurance needs.

Bundled coverage is not always possible, however, especially when households are large and have multiple insurance needs. Some of your insurance coverage, such as life, health care, and disability may come from your employer under different companies and policies. You remain responsible for knowing and managing this information.

TIP: The high degree of specialization in the insurance industry further complicates the information management requirements. Take inventory of your needs and understand your premiums and deductibles. Know the names of your insurance agents and how to contact them. Keep copies of policies in a safe place.

This module organizes and consolidates your insurance information, making it readily accessible in cases of an emergency or at other stressful times when a search for names, policy numbers, and phone numbers may not serve your best interests. In instances when someone not already familiar with various insurance policies is asked to make important decisions about them, having the information ready at-hand will be invaluable.

Home

Homeowner's Insurance

Mortgage Insurance

Renter's Insurance

My Notes

Health and Life

family member's name

**Primary
Health Insurance**

**Supplemental
Health Insurance**

Dental Coverage

Other Coverage

Life Insurance

Disability Insurance

**Long-Term
Care Insurance**

Health and Life

family member's name

Primary Health Insurance

Supplemental Health Insurance

Dental Coverage

Other Coverage

Life Insurance

Disability Insurance

Long-Term Care Insurance

Beneficiaries

Primary Beneficiary

Secondary Beneficiary

My Notes

Business

Primary

Secondary

My Notes

Vehicles

Vehicle One

Vehicle Two

Vehicle Three

Motorcycles

Boat

My Notes

LifeBook

Notes

Notes

LifeBook

Personal Records Module

 Passwords / Access Codes

 Family

 Household Confidants

 Special Days

 Travel

Personal Records

This module captures personal records, including names of family members and close friends and their contact information, special days, and other information regarding your family and social network that you may wish to have on hand. If it's important to you to remember and acknowledge important dates pertaining to your family members and household associates, this is the place to record birthdays, anniversaries, memorials, and other major events in their lives.

You may want to include email addresses, phone numbers, mailing addresses, and social network websites so that the module serves also as a mini-directory for personal contacts. Depending upon your social network, the module has the potential to be quite large and may require a large number of initial entries. A highlight of the module is that changes can be made quickly and easily.

This module also is the place to put miscellaneous record-keeping data, including the passwords and access codes for your online accounts and membership organizations. Much of this information is PRIVATE and should be kept safe for identity security purposes.

TIP: This module is not a substitute for an alphabetical directory. Enter only data that is pertinent for the management of your household. For example, the contact information for close friends who are routinely asked to house-sit or pet-sit in your absence might be recorded here.

Passwords and Access Codes

Professional Membership Passwords

Online Shopping Passwords

Passwords (Netflix, Online Gaming, etc.)

My Notes

Family

family member's name

Birth Certificates

Social Security Number (and Card Location)

Family Member's Contact Information

Family Emergency Numbers

My Notes

family

family member's name

Birth Certificates

**Social Security Number
(and Card Location)**

**Family Member's
Contact Information**

**Family Emergency
Numbers**

My Notes

Family

family member's name

Birth Certificates

Social Security Number (and Card Location)

Family Member's Contact Information

Family Emergency Numbers

My Notes

LifeBook

Family

family member's name

Birth Certificates

Social Security Number (and Card Location)

Family Member's Contact Information

Family Emergency Numbers

My Notes

Household Confidantes

Name and Contact Information

Name and Contact Information

Name and Contact Information

Name and Contact Information

My Notes

LifeBook

Birthdays

Travel

Travel Agent

Online Booking Agencies

Airline Frequent Flyer Numbers

Hotel Rewards Numbers

My Notes

Notes

LifeBook

Pet
Care
Module

Pet One

Pet Two

Pet Care

Our pets are special members of the family. The purpose of this module is to help you organize the information you need to keep them healthy and happy and to make it easy to arrange for their care when you're out of town.

Record the pertinent information about their food and medications so you and others know what they need on-hand on a daily basis. Record contact information for your primary veterinarian as well as your emergency/back-up veterinarian so it's easy to contact them when you need them.

Recording information about boarding options will make it easier to plan and arrange your out-of-town trips.

Pet
One

Food Brand Name

Food Location

Feeding Times
and Quantity

Medication Names
and Dosages

Medication Location

Location of Medication
Hard Copy Paperwork

Veterinarian Name and
Contact Information

module continues the next page

Directions to Veterinarian's Office

Emergency / Back-Up Veterinarian's Name and Contact Information

Kennel Name and Contact Information

Directions to Kennel Location

Immunization Records

My Notes

Pet
Two _____

Food Brand Name

Food Location

Feeding Times and Quantity

Medication Names and Dosages

Medication Location

Location of Medication Hard Copy Paperwork

Veterinarian Name and Contact Information

module continues the next page

Directions to Veterinarian's Office

Emergency / Back-Up Veterinarian's Name and Contact Information

Kennel Name and Contact Information

Directions to Kennel Location

Immunization Records

My Notes

Notes

Notes

Professional Home Services Module

 Communication & Entertainment Systems

 Trades Persons

 Home Maintenance

 Other Professional Services

Professional Home Services

Most of us engage professional services to maintain our homes, health, vehicles, and legal affairs. In some cases, we may only need a service once, but we typically schedule our professional help on a regular or recurring basis. It will help to have on-hand the most recent contact information for your various service providers and to create a service schedule so that you can plan accordingly.

In this module, you can identify the professional services you commonly use, enter and update their contact information, and record appointment schedules as they take shape.

Your efforts to keep this section up-to-date will be rewarded whenever you seek help from your service providers. Once you have identified the most qualified professionals, keeping their contact information current will be of great value, allowing you to reach them as needed and also to share this information with friends and families.

When recording data for service providers, you may have varying needs and contact information for different family members. We have included multiple data input pages for this purpose.

Be sure to make a note of your last appointment or service date, as well as any upcoming scheduled dates. This kind of information is handy to have in the event that questions arise about past or future service.

TIP: You may want to duplicate some of this contact information in other **LifeBook** modules when it applies to specific household appliances, digital devices, or vehicles.

Communications and Entertainment Systems

Telephone Service

Internet Provider

Cable or Satellite Service

My Notes

Trades Persons

Carpenter / Builder

Electrician

Plummer

Painter

Heating and Air Conditioning / Repair

My Notes

LifeBook

Home Maintenance

Cleaning Service

Landscape Service

Pest Control

My Notes

Other
Professional Services

Attorney

Realtor

Car Mechanic

My Notes

Notes

Notes

LifeBook

Schools Module

 School Information

 Online Instruction

 Extra Curricular Activities

Schools

The idea of packing the kids off to school and leaving them for the day in the hands of their teachers is a thing of the past. If you're the parent of a school-age child, you have lots of information to manage—meetings, contacts, appointments, field trips, sports events, and so forth. It's not always possible to organize things in advance because schedules change so fast. But it's helpful to have on-hand certain types of information to help you stay on top of things. That includes basic information such as how to reach the school principal or teacher when your child is ill and unable to attend classes. Other information may relate to extracurricular activities or to the computer and mobile technologies your child uses in school. This module provides a place to record and keep track of such information.

One of the proven measures of success in the performance of a student is how well she or he manages their time and organizes the flow of work in their classes. This module is designed to help you and your child-student manage these important factors. Multiple data tabs are provided beneath most entry headings so that you can organize your information for multiple students or schools.

School Information

family member's name

Name of School

Names and Contact Information of the School Office Secretaries

Contact Information of School Principal

Names and Contact Information of the School Primary Teacher

My Notes

School Information

family member's name

Name of School

Names and Contact Information of the School Office Secretaries

Contact Information of School Principal

Names and Contact Information of the School Primary Teacher

My Notes

Online Instruction

family member's name

Name and Contact Information of Online Instructor

Name of Online Computer System

Online Computer System Password

Online Computer System Technical Support

My Notes

Extracurricular Activity

family member's name

Contact Information of Sports Coaches

Practice and Event Schedules

Contact Information of Music / Band Director

Practice and Event Schedules

Other Extracurricular Activities

Parent-Teacher Association Contact Information

My Notes

Extracurricular Activity

family member's name

Contact Information of Sports Coaches

Practice and Event Schedules

Contact Information of Music / Band Director

Practice and Event Schedules

Other Extracurricular Activities

Parent-Teacher Association Contact Information

My Notes

Notes

LifeBook

Vehicles Module

Vehicle One

Vehicle Two

Vehicle Three

Road Service

Vehicles

Most of us own at least one motor vehicle and many families typically maintain multiple vehicles. Some of us also own boats, RVs and motorcycles. Managing our vehicles can be a sizable responsibility and some of us function as the household "fleet manager."

The ownership title and other documentation for each vehicle should be kept in a safe location, its registration and insurance renewed periodically, and regular maintenance and repair service scheduled, completed, and documented. A good starting point for these tasks is a method of maintaining the various types of information for each vehicle. This module is designed to help you do just that.

TIP: Storing Vehicle Titles and Other Documents

If you've ever had to replace a lost vehicle title you know it's a major inconvenience. You also know it takes time to obtain a new title, which is problematic because you usually need the title right away when transferring ownership or selling a vehicle. Keep titles, copies of your vehicle registrations, and other pertinent documentation in a safe place and record the location in your LifeBook.

Maintenance and Repairs

Proper maintenance is essential to a vehicle's dependable and safe operation as well as for maximizing its resale value. This can be the most challenging aspect of vehicle ownership. A vehicle's age and mileage determine the amount of time, attention, and money that is required to keep it safely on the road. The key to staying on top of scheduled maintenance, as well as repair needs and expenses, is to keep on file the customer copies of repair orders from your service garages. Keep this information in separate folders for each vehicle and organize it for periodic review. This will help you in the following ways:

- You'll know when the next scheduled maintenance is due.
- You'll know which minor and major repairs have been completed.
- You'll be able to track your vehicle expenses. This can also help you make decisions about keeping or replacing a vehicle.
- If you decide to sell a vehicle, providing complete service records to a prospective buyer is a strong selling feature. It can even help you command a higher price.

Vehicle One

Vehicle Make, Model, Year

Title / Registration and Insurance Document Location

Names and Contact Information of Service Providers

Names and Contact Information of Insurance Agency

Insurance Policy Number

My Notes

Vehicle One

Vehicle Make, Model, Year

Title / Registration and Insurance Document Location

Names and Contact Information of Service Providers

Names and Contact Information of Insurance Agency

Insurance Policy Number

My Notes

Vehicle Three

Vehicle Make, Model, Year

Title / Registration and Insurance Document Location

Names and Contact Information of Service Providers

Names and Contact Information of Insurance Agency

Insurance Policy Number

My Notes

Roadside Service

**Towing Service
Contact Information**

**Roadside Assistance
Policy Number**

My Notes

Notes

Emergencies Module

 Law Enforcement

 Natural Event

 Other Emergencies

Emergencies

When an emergency occurs, you need to respond quickly and effectively. Your local 911 service provides immediate access to first responders in the case of serious and imminent danger. So you should always call 911 first when emergency assistance is needed so the professional operator can determine what responders are needed and quickly dispatch them to your location.

You may also need the direct phone numbers of emergency responders in less critical situations. For example, who do you call to remove a fallen tree that is blocking the road?

LifeBook can be a lifesaver if you record all of the emergency phone numbers you may need and know where to find them.

Law Enforcement

City Police

County Sheriff

State Highway Patrol

My Notes

Law Enforcement

Local Fire Station

Volunteer Fire Brigade

County Forester

Local Road Maintenance

**Local Emergency
Response Office**

My Notes

Other Emergencies

Road Service

Natural Gas Service

Water Service

Electricity Service

My Notes

23406511R00081

Printed in Great Britain
by Amazon